PUFFIN BOOKS

# HORACE WAS A HAPPY HORSE
### AND OTHER SILLY VERSES

An irresistible collection of poetry drawn from Finola Akister's two books *Before You Grow Up* and *Before You Go To Bed*. Unusual pets, strange guests for tea, giraffes with sore throats and a baby kangaroo with *very* cold feet are among the nonsensical gems found in this delightful anthology. New twists to old rhymes, narrative poems in the tradition of Hilaire Belloc and short snappy nonsense rhymes, make this an accessible book for younger children and grown-ups who yearn for the fun of childhood.

Finola Akister originally wrote the poems in this double collection to entertain her two grandsons. She died in 1992.

Colin West is well known as a writer and collector of nonsense and verse, as well as a popular comic illustrator.

Finola Akister

# Horace was a Happy Horse
## and *Other Silly Verses*

Illustrated by Colin West

PUFFIN BOOKS

PUFFIN BOOKS

Published by the Penguin Group
Penguin Books Ltd, 27 Wrights Lane, London W8 5TZ, England
Penguin Books USA Inc., 375 Hudson Street, New York, New York 10014, USA
Penguin Books Australia Ltd, Ringwood, Victoria, Australia
Penguin Books Canada Ltd, 10 Alcorn Avenue, Toronto, Ontario, Canada M4V 3B2
Penguin Books (NZ) Ltd, 182–190 Wairau Road, Auckland 10, New Zealand

Penguin Books Ltd, Registered Offices: Harmondsworth, Middlesex, England

*Before You Grow Up* first published by Viking Kestrel 1987
Published in Puffin Books 1989
Text copyright © Finola Akister, 1987
Illustrations copyright © Colin West, 1987

*Before You To Bed* first published by Viking Kestrel 1989
Published in Puffin Books 1990
Text copyright © Finola Akister, 1989
Illustrations copyright © Colin West, 1989

Published in Puffin Books in one volume 1993
10 9 8 7 6 5 4 3 2 1

Printed in England by Clays Ltd, St Ives plc
Filmset in Century Schoolbook

# Contents

# Before You Grow Up

A butterfly just fluttered by
And settled on a rose.
Where it came from I don't know,
I cannot say where it will go,
For suddenly it flew away.
But still, I'm glad it came today.

Always it amazes me
How slippery the soap can be.
I pick it up and start to rub,
When WHOOSH – it jumps into the tub.
I search and search and search around:
That bar of soap just can't be found.
Instead of lying in the dish,
It's swimming round, just like a fish.
I cannot catch it – golly gosh,
I think I'll go without a wash.

It was early in the morning,
Just as the day was dawning,
That Fido packed his bone and ran away.
But, realizing what he'd done,
He thought it wasn't much like fun,
So he turned about and hurried home next day.

$C$ats like milk.

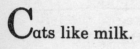

Mice like cheese.

Little dogs like sausagees.

Crabs always walk sideways, and so
Spare a thought for this unhappy plight.
If a left-handed crab always walked to the left,
And his true love was geared to the right,

They would pass by like ships in the night.
Just a wave as they hove into view,
Destined never to walk side by side, or to talk
Claw in claw, like the other crabs do.

The solution is not hard to find,
And matters could be so much worse —
There's the chance they could meet on the
  strand or the street.
If one of them walked in reverse.

Zanzibar was a very large lion,
With a beautiful lion-like mane.
He looked very fierce, ferocious and wild,
Though, in fact, he was terribly tame.

His grandad was born in the jungle,
Where the weather was sultry and hot.
But Zanzibar knew, as he gazed round the zoo,
That, in England, the weather was not.

He thought, with his lion-like thinking,
As he lazily gazed round the zoo,
How happy he'd be, if he only were free.
He was bored. There was nothing to do.

He longed, with his lion-like longing,
To go for a stroll round about.
His cage was too small – there was no room at
  all –
But his keeper would not let him out.

Zanzibar scowled at the keeper,
In his lion-like sort of way.
Should I eat him? he thought. But he'd have to
  be caught.
And the keeper kept out of his way.

So Zanzibar lay there and brooded,
Till one day – it was just getting dark –
They hustled him into a lorry
And drove him away to a park.

Now Zanzibar gazes about him.
He is pleased with this lovely new place.
He lies on the grass with a lion-type lass
And a smile on his lion-like face.

There is one thing I cannot do
Because, you see, I'm only two.
No matter how I try and try,
It nearly always makes me cry.
I don't know when it all began,
Or why some very clever man
Thought that buttons could be fun –
I simply can't get mine undone.
My mother comes and helps me out,
But, really, what's it all about?
Although I try, it's all in vain.
I just can't do them up again.

He was small and white,
With eyes so bright,
But he wandered away from the house.
He was small and sweet,
So if you should meet,
Please bring me back my mouse.

I'll polish up the teapot, thought Sarah Jane
one night.
Mummy will be so surprised to see it shining
  bright.
She found the cloth for polishing, and then, with
  might and main,
She rubbed it once, and just for luck she rubbed
  it once again.

Sarah Jane was worried that she hadn't done it
  right,
For as she rubbed, with might and main, there
  came a blinding light.
And standing there before her was a giant, ten
  feet tall.
He was smiling down upon her, which made her
  feel so small.

His mighty arms were folded on his very mighty
   chest.
He wore a turban on his head and jewels on his
   vest.
His shoes were just like gravy boats, and
   everybody knows

That shoes like that are always made with
  funny curled-up toes.

Sarah Jane was speechless, so great was her
  surprise.
She gazed upon the giant – she could not believe
  her eyes.
His arms unfolded slowly, then he waved one
  mighty hand:
'I am the Teapot Genie, and I wait for your
  command.'

Sarah Jane had heard about the Genie of the
  Ring.
She had heard about the Genie of the Lamp and
  everything.
But she had never thought that teapots had a
  genie too –
She'd heard of 'instant', 'quick' and 'fine' but not
  of 'genie' brew.

'Please, could I have a teddy bear?' asked little
  Sarah J.
At once, with just a puff of smoke, the Genie
  went away.
Sarah Jane woke up and found that she was still
  in bed.
It must have been a dream – but what was this
  beside her head?

It was a lovely teddy bear and just exactly
  right.
She wondered where it came from 'cause it
  wasn't there last night.
It's very, very strange, and Sarah Jane cannot
  explain.
She isn't even sure herself from where her teddy
  came.

It came down from the ceiling
On a silken, single thread.
I screamed out loud
Because I don't
Like spiders in my bed.

# Lots of spots

Are polka dots.

An elephant, they said, had come to see me in
the morning.
I thought it very odd that this should be.
I was surprised – no, even more, I was certain, I
was *sure*
That I didn't know an elephant, so how could
one know me?

I didn't like to tell them that I didn't know an
elephant,
So I pretended that it wasn't strange to me,
And I made it very plain that, should he ever
call again,
I'd be obliged if they would ask him in for tea.

It's very odd, they said, that I was friendly with
an elephant.
It might seem odd to them, but not to me.
They hinted I was lying and remarked, 'Perhaps
a lion
Or a hippopotamus might come along and want
some tea.'

'I am not,' I said, 'acquainted with a single
hippopotamus,
And a lion is an animal with whom I disagree.
The monkeys that I knew are really very, very
few,
But an elephant is different and should be asked
to tea.'

Still I couldn't make them see that elephants
were different.
Perhaps it's just as well, you will agree,
For I really do not know a single elephant,
and so
They will never be obliged to ask my elephant
to tea.

The tortoise moves, but slowly,
As he goes from A to B.
He takes his time along the way,
But what he thinks, I cannot say
Because (it's very sad to tell)
He never comes out of his shell.

He never rushes, I am told,
Or runs on recklessly.
What his pace is I don't know,
But I am certain it is slow.
Why he lingers I can't say —
It must be 'cause he's made that way.

The tortoise moves, but slowly.
It is obvious that he
Has got a heavy load to bear.
He takes it with him everywhere.
The house he carries on his back
Must be a heavy handicap.

The tortoise moves, but slowly,
As he plods from A to B.
He crawls along from day to day,
Slowly but surely on his way.
He stops – I don't know what he thinks.
Perhaps he's having forty winks.

Yes, the tortoise moves so slowly:
He seems to lack the pace.
I asked him, was he good or bad,
Was he happy, was he sad?
He said he didn't want to tell,
And disappeared inside his shell.

The tortoise does not move at all
From A or B or C.
It's winter, and the snow came down.
He didn't laugh or smile or frown
But, slow and steady, he did creep
Into his shell, and fell asleep.

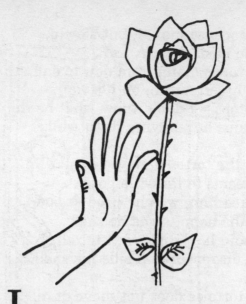

I saw a lovely rose one day,
As I was passing on my way,
But when I tried to pick it, oh,
It pricked my little finger so.
I will not pick a rose again.
Instead I'll make a daisy chain.

$M$y bedroom gets into a mess.
I tidy up and then
The next day it is just as bad,
So I tidy up again.

If I could choose
What I would be,
I'd like to be a bumble bee.
I'd bumble in and out of flowers,
But only during sunny hours,
For if it rained hard, you can bet
I'd bumble off and not get wet.

When I was just a foal,
My mother said to me,
'Always do as you are told,
And never disagree.'
I'd like to do just as she said –
There isn't any doubt –
But whenever I open my mouth to say, 'Yes,'
It's always a 'Neigh' that comes out.

Neigh!

If, walking down a busy street,
It happens that you chance to meet
A tiger,
You must be discreet.
But
If it is a pussy cat,
By all means stop and have a chat.

A camel can race through the desert
Because everyone knows
He doesn't get hot,
Or bothered a lot,
By sand between his toes.

You have heard of the ugly duckling
Who turned into a beautiful swan.
But have you heard
Of the ugly swan
Who had rotten luck
And didn't turn into
A beautiful duck?

They look like little baskets,
Hanging up there in the tree.
I know that they are birds' nests,
But I think you will agree
That if their owners spent more time
And built a little roof,
Nests really would be warmer
And much more weather-proof.

33

The mule is a beast of burden.
He is strong, but he's obstinate too.
If he's bearing a grudge,
And unwilling to budge,
There is nothing at all you can do.

Just when I thought I had made it,
And it really was looking so grand,
I picked up my model kit aeroplane –
Then it all fell apart in my hand.

I wash my face – that's easy –
Though sometimes I have fears:
Mum says she could grow potatoes
In the space behind my ears.

I've thought and thought about it,.
And it might be just as well,
If I took some care, while the soap is there,
To wash that space as well.

When we go on a trip to the seaside,
My mum and dad take my hand.
Because it's in reach, we go down to the beach
And make castles with buckets of sand.

Mum takes a case to this heavenly place.
It is packed tight with goodies to eat.
Dad digs a hole, with the zest of a mole,
Then the tide comes and tickles my feet.

But when we get home to the garden,
Dad's fervour for digging is slack.
He puts down the spade, goes and sits in the
  shade
And explains that he's got a bad back.

The tide comes in
Upon the shore.
It turns about.
The tide goes out.

I have a lovely car, you know.
I get in it and go, go, go.
Near and far, up and down,
I travel all around the town.
I toot my horn (it's only fair
To let the people know I'm there).
Even on hills I do not shirk,
Though pedalling up hills is hard work.

I try not to paddle in puddles,
And I try to eat cabbage as well.
I try to be good 'cause I know that I should,
So why I am bad I can't tell.

It's just that a puddle is tempting,
And cabbage, I think, is a mess.
I'll have to start walking round puddles
And swallow the cabbage, I guess.

They tell me an elephant never forgets,
And, of course, what they say may be so.
That's all very well, but how can they tell?
I mean, how can they possibly know?

The extraordinary thing about daisies –
I must make this abundantly plain –
Is they're mowed with the lawn
(You can't see one at all),
But the next day they're all back again.

The barn owl looked out through his spectacled
  eyes,
And he gazed at the farmyard below.
The sun was beginning to rise in the east,
And the cock was beginning to crow.
It is time, thought the owl, I was going to sleep.
He was old, he was wise and he knew
That for him it was right. He'd been up half the
  night
Serenading that girl owl with two things in
  sight,
Namely, to-whit and to-woo.

Dog was a stray with nowhere to stay.
He just wandered about in the street.
He spent every day in the usual way,
Just looking for something to eat.

He wasn't to blame 'cause he hadn't a name,
Though he desperately wished that he had.
He never had known a name of his own.
He was lonely and hungry and sad.

One day, without warning, at ten in the
  morning,
He walked up to a cottage and found
Something really appalling – a lady had fallen
And lay in a heap on the ground.

The lady was old and she seemed very cold.
Dog had to get help, that was plain.
Without waiting to stop, he ran to the shop
And barked loudly, again and again.

'It's that black-and-white stray. I will chase him
   away,'
Said a tall man who looked very grand.
But a woman said, 'Stay, he is trying to say
Something we don't understand.'

'I think that I know,' said the man. 'Let us go.'
Then they followed Dog out of the door.
The old lady they found. She was still on the
  ground –
She was lying there, just as before.

There was a bump on her head, so they put her
  to bed,
And soon she recovered and cried,
'How lucky am I that you chanced to pass by.
But for you I would surely have died.'

'It was not just by chance,' said the man, with a
  glance
At the lady who lay in the bed.

' 'Twas the stray dog that cried, brought us here
  to your side,
So you really should thank him instead.'

Then the old lady knew what she wanted to do,
And she smiled. It was lovely to see.
'If the dog is a stray, don't send him away.
Bring him in. He shall live here with me.'

Dog has got his desire as he lies by the fire,
For the days of his hardship are past.
He is pleased to claim that he now has a name:
It is Ben, and he's happy at last.

Humpty Dumpty sat on a wall.
He fell, so now I can see
Why all the king's horses
And all the king's men
Had scrambled egg for tea.

Jack and Jill walked up the hill,
Then they had to stop.
There was nowhere else for them to go –
They had reached the very top.

They take me here,
They take me there,
They take me almost everywhere.
But wherever they take me,
Wherever I roam,
I'm just a homing pigeon,
So I am going home.

If you should see a little dog
(He's sort of black, but here and there,
Just mixed amongst the black,
You'll find odd spots of brownish hair),

Perhaps he isn't really lost.
He just strayed off the other day.
I'm certain that he would come home
If only he could find his way.

I do not wish to be a fish.
I might end up upon a dish.
But, worse than that, if I should linger,
I might become a fried fish finger.

The good things are bad,
If you see what I mean,
Like chocolates and toffees
And cakes full of cream.
They are bad for your teeth,
And they make you grow fat,
Then they spoil your complexion.
Just think about that.

The Vikings sailed across the sea.
Each man pulled upon his oar.
Without a doubt they were all tired out
When they reached the foreign shore.

After a rest they fought with zest.
They won but, alas and alack,
They had to stay — there was no other way.
They were all too tired to row back.

54

They said that there were fairies at the bottom of the garden,
And I thought I'd go along so I could see
Just what a fairy looked like, 'cause I'd never come across one,
And I really longed to see just how a fairy ought to be.

Though I didn't see a fairy at the bottom of the garden
(So what a fairy looks like I really cannot say),
I think perhaps they do live at the bottom of the garden
But now, because it's summer, they've gone off on holiday.

I'm looking out the window.
I'm feeling kind of blue.
I've played at trains and lots of games,
Now I don't know what to do.
The cat's gone out. Without a doubt,
She's catching mice again.
The puppy dog has gone to sleep.
I wish it would not rain.

I've read the jolly comic book
I got from Auntie Kit.
I've tried to do the jigsaw,
But the pieces will not fit.
I've been and asked my mother
If she'd like to come and play,
But she says she's much too busy.
And the rain won't go away.

I've chatted to the goldfish,
But it doesn't make a sound.
It really doesn't do a thing
Except swim round and round.
Oh, how I wish that somebody
Would come along and play,
And how I want the sun to shine
And chase the rain away.

When it was my birthday,
Daddy asked what I would choose
For a special birthday present,
So I answered, 'Dancing shoes.'

We went to town to buy some,
But they cost an awful lot.
'Have you any cheaper?' Daddy asked,
But that was all they'd got.

So Daddy had to pay the price,
Though he made an awful fuss.
'I'm glad you're a little girl,' he said,
'And not an octopus.'

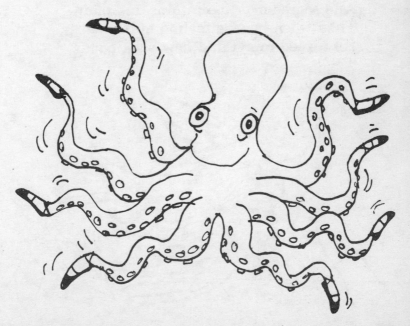

An eagle flew out of his eyrie,
And soared over mountains and plain,
Then when he was feeling quite weary,
He turned round and flew back again.

My roller skates won't ever do
The simple things I want them to.
I put them on and try my best,
But one goes East and the other goes West.

I often fall upon the floor,
Then, full of pluck, I try once more.
But my roller skates think they know best:
One still goes East and the other goes West.

Should you wish to see a crocodile,
You'll find one swiming in the Nile.
But think before you seek one out –
Their manners leave much room for doubt.
They're slinky creatures, full of guile,
And have a most preposterous smile.
I've heard it said, and think it's true,
There are some dreadful things they do.
They care not what or who you are
And are not too particular
About the menu for their tea –
They eat up anything they see.

So if, by chance, it happens you
Are wondering what is best to do,
Don't paddle near this carnivore
But safely stay upon the shore.
Throw him a bun or two and say,
'Good morning, how are you today?'
But take my warning. Do not forget:
Never keep one as a pet.

A mother bird sat in the nest
And said to her fledglings, 'Cheep, cheep.'
Roughly translated, her words meant this:
You must look before you leap.

Rings go round,
Squares are square,

But whirlygigs
Go everywhere.

$I$f you stumble and tumble,

And you're not very tall,

You won't have very far to fall.

Will you give me a clue
As to what I should do
When I'm sent up to bed without tea?
Do I sit there and cry?
Or look out at the sky?
Oh why does this happen to me?
It's no good being haughty –
I really was naughty.
I should never have eaten that jam.
And I have to confess,
I made rather a mess
When I carved up the rest of the ham.
But when all's done and said
I sit here on my bed . . .
I'll be better tomorrow I vow.
But consider my plight:
I get no tea tonight,
And I'm ever so hungry right now.

If I was a cat,
I'd sit on the mat
And chat
To the mouse
Who lived in the house.
But
If I was the mouse
Who lived in the house,
I doubt if I'd feel
Like having
A chat
With the cat
Who sat on the mat.

If you should go to the Isle of Man,
And you should see a cat
Without a tail, don't be surprised,
Manx cats are made like that.

I know I have to go to bed.
I do not want to sleep,
For Santa Claus comes here tonight,
And I want to have a peep.

If I was very rich,
I'd walk into a shop.
I'd buy myself potato crisps
And then a lollipop.

I'd buy some pink ice-cream for you
And then some sweets for me.
But, alas, I am not very rich —
I've only got ten p.

Hey diddle diddle, the cat had a fiddle
And played it all day and all night.
Then, before very long, he burst into song,
Which, of course, gave the neighbours a fright.

The loud caterwauling was really appalling.
The noise rent the air like a knife.
The neighbours would hoot him. They
   threatened to shoot him.
So the cat had to run for his life.

I travel slowly, but I go
From here to there, and though I'm slow,
I always, always leave a trail.
I have to 'cause I am a snail.

I said I'd do my homework
(There was an awful lot),
But I forgot.
I said I'd write a thank-you note
For the present from Auntie Dot,
But I forgot.

I should have been quite sorry,
And I was, but not a lot,
'Cause I forgot.

Now I'm being good as gold,
So Mum won't be upset.
Tomorrow is my birthday.
I do hope she won't forget.

The camel has a funny lump,
Which everybody calls a hump.
He carries it upon his back.
It's like a sort of storage pack.
So he can live a long, long time
Without the need to stop and dine.
In deserts, if you stop to think,
There's nowhere he can get a drink,
And as the sun is very hot,
He's happy with the hump he's got.

He is just a fluffy chicken.
He is only one day old.
His beak is sort of yellow.
The rest of him is gold.
'Cheep, cheep,' is all he says.
It doesn't mean a lot.
But it's all that he can utter.
It's all the speech he's got.

He said his name was Walter.
He was a cross-bred hound.
He read the 'Welcome' on the mat,
So he wandered in to have a chat.
He told them he was just a stray,
And said that he would like to stay,
So Walter never went away.

I have ten fingers and ten toes.
It's just the right amount.
Apart from other useful things,
They help me when I count.

Is Archibald just a cat?
An ordinary tabby cat?
No! Archibald is more than that.

He has the habits, it is true,
Of doing things that most cats do,
But Archibald is something new . . .

Archibald belongs to me,
Which makes him special, don't you see?
I love him so, and he loves me.

I don't remember being one
Because I was so very young.
Then being two I don't recall

Because I was still very small.
The nicest year of all is three
'Cause now I can remember me.

I stand and stare. I can't believe
I'm seeing what I see.
A cow, dressed in a jumper,
Is walking straight at me.

Though odd, I agree, I'm beginning to see
The reason for it now.
The cow is wearing a jumper
Because she's a Jersey cow.

A bee, a very busy bee,
Was great on hospitality.
When she invited friends to dine
She gave them mead (a honey wine).
Her hive, it seemed, was not, alas,
Equipped throughout with British Gas.
There was no way that she could cook,
Nor did she have a cooking book.

Undaunted by this state of things,
She thought it out, then spread her wings.
She travelled far, she travelled near,
And then engaged a caterer.
It goes to show how much she cared –
She really was a bee prepared.

The moon peeped through the window.
I was lying in my bed.
It was very bright that starry night,
So I opened a book and read.

# Before You Go To Bed

I woke up in the morning
Feeling kind of 'off'.
Will I develop lots of spots
Or just a nasty cough?
But then my best friend called to see
If I'd go out to play.
Suddenly I felt ever so well –
One does on Saturday.

'I have a very sore throat,' said Jemima,
'And I'm in so much terrible pain,
My voice has gone scratchy and squeaky,
Will I ever get better again?'
'It will take a long time,' said her doctor,
'It's a thing at which no one should laugh,
It's the worst sort of germ you could possibly have,
As you happen to be a giraffe.'

I had a little tadpole,
I found it in a bog.
Some legs it grew and then I knew
I had a little frog.

Where can I locate an ant-eater?
I've never seen one about town.
And the ants' nests that litter my garden
Are undoubtedly getting me down.

If you happen to see such a creature
Will you stop him, and just to please me,
Invite him to dine, he can come any time,
For breakfast or dinner or tea.

Mary, Mary, quite contrary,
How does your garden fare?
'Well the plants grow I guess,
But I have to confess,
I've got thousands of weeds everywhere.'

There's a very, very pretty rose
In the hedge for all to see.
They've told me it's a wild rose,
But it looks quite tame to me.

Roses are red
Violets are blue
I don't really think that's right,
Do you?
Some roses are red
I guess that's true,
But violets are violet —
BLUEBELLS are blue.

Chomp, chomp, went the caterpillar
Till he'd eaten all the leaf.
Then because there was nothing to cling to
He fell to the ground underneath.

If you have a nice voice and you sing like a lark,
Or some other bird you might hear in the park,
You can break into song at the drop of a hat
But, not if you happen to sing like a cat.
A cat sings his songs in the dead of the night.
It is not like the music Beethoven would write.
It's a horrible noise, now I come to recall,
It's not really like any music at all.

Mary had a little lamb
Its fleece she went and sold.
Now she has a woolly jumper,
But the lamb is feeling cold.

The other day I chanced to see
A pussy-cat who winked at me.
I said, 'Hello, I hope you're well,'
But what he answered I couldn't tell.
He said 'Meow', but you can see
It didn't mean a thing to me.
I asked him, in a friendly way,
How many mice he'd caught that day.
But again he only said 'Meow'
Which didn't mean a lot somehow.
To show how friendly I could be
I asked him would he come to tea.
'Meow' was all he said, and then
I noticed that he winked again.
I could not understand this cat.
In school they taught me this and that,
But not what one should do or say
To a cat one meets upon the way.
I wasn't getting anywhere
So I said 'Goodbye' and left him there.

Ding-dong bell
Puss is in the well.
She jumped in by the merest whim
And then found out she could not swim.

My mother was a blackbird,
She lived up in a tree.
She laid an egg,
She kept it warm,
It hatched
And there was
Me.

There's a special chair in our house,
It's Daddy's chair.
There's another one just like it,
And my mum sits there.
There's a special chair for Grandad,
Then the one for Gran makes four,
I haven't got a special chair
So I sit on the floor.

Mirror high upon the wall,
What use are you to me?
You're fine for people who are tall,
But I'm only three foot three.

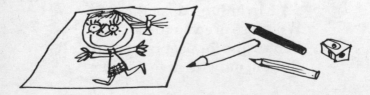

I picked up a pencil to draw
A picture to hang on the wall.
A portrait of Dad, but it really was bad,
It didn't look like him at all.
Then Dad said that he'd draw a picture of me –
He picked up the pencil and tried,
It was such a mess that I have to confess
That we laughed and we laughed till we cried.

I was playing with my train set
One rainy afternoon,
When all at once I saw a mouse
Was running round the room.
I didn't quite know what to do,
I thought of this and that,
Then the mouse ran up to me and said,
'Please save me from the cat.'
So I hid the little fellow,
He had such appealing eyes.
And Puss Cat never knew
That I had robbed him of his prize.
I gave the cat some extra food
To try and make amends,
But I dare not ever tell him
That the mouse and I are friends.

The pitter-patter of tiny feet
Ran quickly across the floor,
They pitted and they patted
Till they reached the pantry door.
I'd been asleep before the fire –
It was comfy and warm on the mat.
I didn't bother to chase that mouse,
Because I'm a lazy cat.

I got up in the morning,
Put on my coat and hat,
I trotted off to market
To purchase 'This' and 'That'.
Now 'This' was very easy –
I bought it straight away,
But 'That' was much more difficult –
There was none about that day.
So I went off home without 'That',
It was not what I would wish,
Because I had to eat my chips
Without some lovely fish.

It was an early day in spring
I saw the most amazing thing.
A singing thrush just flying by
Stopped as this strange thing caught his eye.
Then out of curiosity
Flew down to earth and sat by me.
An earthworm popped out of his hole,
Then next to him a furry mole.
A rabbit, much to his surprise,
Said he could not believe his eyes.
A wasp and then a busy bee
Buzzed down to see what they could see.
A fox and lots of angry hounds
Came rushing up in leaps and bounds,

Then quickly stopped and joined the throng
That gazed on this phenomenon.
Horses came and horsemen too
Joined with this mixed and motley crew,
Who stood around and gazed in awe
Upon the strange thing that they saw.
I did not know what it could be –
It was a perfect mystery.
Then with a sort of purring sound
It lifted quickly from the ground.
It flew away at such a pace
And soon was lost in outer space.

If you don't want to go
And you really don't know
How to get there
Or how to come back,
You might as well stay
Where you happen to be,
But perhaps you prefer
To go off on a spree.
If you don't know the way
And you want to explore,
You can ask someone clever
Who's been there before.
If they won't tell you
Don't cry in dismay,
If you look at the map
It will show you the way.

'I'd like to go outside,'
Said Jane one sunny day.
'But first I'll ask my mother
If I can go out to play.
I think my mother will agree
But if it starts to rain,
I won't stay out and get all wet,
I'll come back in again.'

Archibald was full of pluck
But, sad to say, had rotten luck.
He wished to travel wide and far
But lacked the vital stamina.
Still, Archibald would not give in
And one day, by the merest whim,
He put on running shoes and shorts
And entered in the local sports.

He was surprised that he'd signed on
To run a five-mile marathon.
He knew before the race began
That he would be an also-ran,
Still none the less and just the same
Our lad was nothing if not game.
He'd have a go but knew he'd lack
The energy to stagger back.

He started with a gentle trot
Like people do who jog a lot.
The first mile almost crippled him,
His body ached in every limb.
But as the lad was full of pluck,
And by the oddest stroke of luck,
It chanced he trod with leaden feet
Upon a dog out in the street,

Who took a quick dislike and more
To this boy who'd trodden on his paw.
So quickly getting to his feet
He chased our hero down the street.
Then, even though the effort hurt,
Young Archibald put on a spurt,
No longer did he merely jog –
He knew he must outrun the dog.
He hurried at so fast a pace
He actually won the race.

Then with the minimum of fuss
Our Archibald went home by bus.

I had a trip upon a ship.
A ride upon a train.
I'll have to do it in reverse
When I go home again.

Luton is an airport.
For aeroplanes no doubt.
They fly them in,
They turn them round,
And then they fly them out.

They fly to other aerodromes
Away across the sea,
They fly them out,
They turn them round,
And then fly back, you see.

'Come fly with me, come fly with me,'
Said the pilot to the crew.
As they were all inside the aeroplane,
There was nothing much else they could do.

London Bridge was taken down,
It's sad, but let me say,
They built it up and it's just like new
In the good old USA.

There's a monster, they think, up in Scotland
That is swimming around in Loch Ness.
And though some people say they have seen it,
There are those who are doubtful, I guess.

But if there's a monster in Scotland
And it's happily swimming about,
There's no cause for alarm, it is doing no harm
If it stays there and doesn't come out.

He would have liked to gallop
For he had to travel far,
But his horse was old and short of breath —
How he wished he had a car!
The day was drawing to a close,
The light was getting dim.
The old horse stumbled, almost fell
And he feared the horse was ill.
Then he knew that he might never
Reach the town at all.
For he was a knight in armour,
And he knew that each (k)night must fall.

'Pardon me, Sir, when I tell you,
There is something I have to relate.
I went for a walk and lingered to talk
To a horse that I met near a gate.
Try to believe when I tell you
This horse was remarkably kind.
In a roundabout way, he warned me to stay
Far away from a thing he had found.
"There is something quite strange in my meadow,
I do not know what it can be,"
Said the horse in a most distressed manner,
"But you're welcome to come in and see.
It looks like a large shiny saucer,"
Said the horse who was showing some fear,
"There's a tiny wee man who keeps bobbing about,
I wish it would all disappear.
What on earth do you think it can be?"
Asked the horse in his kindliest way.
"I fear I don't know," I replied, "Shall we go?
I'm really not eager to stay."
So we left by the gate to the meadow,
And that, Sir, is why you can see
A horse standing here in the classroom,
I brought him along, Sir, with me.
So, pardon me, Sir, when I ask you
To be kind to this horse, for you know,
Until someone gets rid of that thing in his field
This poor horse has nowhere to go.'

If you're going to the moon, you must
Expect to see a lot of dust.
Even worse than that I fear,
There isn't any air up there.
I tell you this for what it's worth,
But I will stay down here on earth.

If walking down a busy road
You chance to meet a big fat toad,
Don't call him 'ugly' on the spot,
You'll hurt his feelings quite a lot.
Just warn him not to linger there –
A car might come from anywhere
And run him down and squash him flat.
The toad, you know, would not like that.

'Do you think,' said the tortoise, 'it would
   matter a lot
If I walked a bit faster? You know,
There are so many places I'm longing to see
And my progress is painfully slow.'
'I think you're supposed to go slow,' said the hare.
'You have legs that are stubby and short,
And that big heavy shell that you carry about
Shows you're really not fashioned for sport.'
The tortoise looked down at his short stubby legs,
It was true, he was built to go slow,
So hard as it seems he abandoned his dreams
Of the places he wanted to go.

'D' is for the Dove of Peace,
It's also for the duck.
There used to be a dodo.
But it died. What rotten luck.

The tiger has stripes all over his coat,
The leopard has spots here and there.
The poor hippopotamus has a proboscis,
The gorilla is covered with hair.
The giraffe has, by heck, a very long neck,
The elephant has a large trunk.
The lion is king of the jungle
But they all run away from the skunk.

Horace was a happy horse
And glad that he was able
To gallop round the fields all day
And sleep all night in the stable.

The yak is a beast that comes from Tibet.
But as I live in England
I haven't seen one yet.

An elephant is big and strong,
Anything he tramples on
Gets squashed.

The polar bear, I'd have you know,
Wears a big fur coat, as white as snow.
It is because, you will agree,
It makes him difficult to see
Amongst the snowflakes on the ground.
He isn't very often found.

I beavered away all the morning,
I beavered the whole day through.
When you happen to be a beaver,
There's nothing much else you can do.

Mrs Bear had hibernated
All the winter through.
She went to bed and slept a lot,
There was nothing else to do.
The ground was cold and frozen hard,
The winds were fierce and chill,
So she and little Baby Bear
Slept on and on, until
One morning Mrs Bear woke up
And she said to herself, said she,
'I think the sun is shining,
I'll just pop out and see.'
So Baby Bear and Mrs Bear
Got up and left their den,
Outside the snow was falling fast
So they went back in again.
'I fear, my dear,' said Mrs Bear,
'It's really very plain,
We have woken up too early,'
So they went to sleep again.

Henry was a grasshopper that hopped around a
    lot.
He never walked sedately, he didn't even trot.
This annoyed the creepie-crawlies
Who liked him . . . not a lot.
He leapt in leaps tremendous,
As high as he could leap.
The little creepie-crawlies
Complained they couldn't sleep,
For he made a noise whilst hopping
Like a sort of chirpy cheep.
Now a frog who would a-wooing go
Stopped wooing for a while.
He had noticed Henry hopping
And he smiled an evil smile . . .
His thoughts were of his dinner
And his heart was full of guile.
But Henry saw the hungry frog
And thought it best to flee.

So he took a leap and leapt into
A cup of lemon tea.
The lady who was drinking it
Exclaimed: 'Oh, deary me,

I didn't ask for sugar,
I declined to have some milk,
But an insect in my lemon tea
Is something I can't drink.'
Then she took the cup and Henry
And she tossed them in the sink.
Henry wasn't pleased at all,
He lost his chirpy cheep.
But he made a vow that in future
He would look before he'd leap.

Nobody really loves me.
I'm not pretty or witty or wise.
They say I am dirty and scorn me,
They say I have got beady eyes.
All that they say may be true –
I'm not going to argue with that –
But I wish someone, somewhere, would love me
For I cannot help being a rat.

The octopus has lots of legs
That grow out at all angles.
One day he tried to cross them
And they finished up all tangles.

You might ask me 'Who am I?'
I'm a very special guy
Who is always dressed in style,
I'll have you know.
I'm not a vulgar sort of chap
Who would wear a woolly cap,
It would look odd in all the places that I go.
Oh yes, I'm really very posh,
I wouldn't wear a mackintosh
Not even if it rained the whole day through.
I'm not the common sort of fellow
Who would tote an umbrella,
I'm particular in everything I do.
There's no need to criticize,
You see I'm very highly prized
And I'm worth much more than you would ever
  think.
I have a twinkle in my eye,
I'm a splendid sort of guy,
I'm stupendous, I'm tremendous,
I'm a mink.

The unicorn had one big horn
In the middle of his head.
It's doubtful if he ever lived,
And if he did, he's dead.

My dog is just a little bit of collie,
Plus a small per cent of beagle, it is true.
There's perhaps a touch of Airedale,
Just a hint of lurcher cur,
And no doubt the merest touch of Kerry blue.
He doesn't look at all like any other dog,
With his hair that grows in little kinky tufts.
They admit that he is clever
But they tell me he will never,
No, he'll positively never be allowed to enter
    Cruft's.
But every night when I come home from school
He runs to meet me, wags his tail with glee,
It's the way that he can say
How much he's missed me all the day,
And that's exactly how I want my dog to be.

If you should notice Montague
When walking down the street,
Don't raise your eyebrows in surprise
At his enormous feet.
Of course they'll grow no bigger
And when Montague grows up,
His feet will match the rest of him,
But now he's just a pup.

'I wish,' said Bunny Rabbit,
'I could climb into a tree,
Like my good friend Sammy Squirrel
Who lives quite close to me.
His house is up a tree you know
And he can see all round,
But I can't see as much as him,
'Cause I'm standing on the ground.
Sometimes Sammy asks me
If I'd like to go to tea.
I have to say I'm sorry
But I cannot, don't you see,
I'd like to go to tea with you
But I cannot climb your tree.
You have such sharp and clinging claws
But I have only paddy paws,
And little rabbits, such as me,
Were never meant to climb a tree.'

Some things tend to puzzle me,
Then I want to know,
Why hares can run so very fast,
Why tortoises are slow.
Why all giraffes are tall and thin,
Why the walrus is so fat,
Or why I have to eat my greens?
Are the things I wonder at.

Cornelius made such a fuss
When told to eat his greens.
He didn't like the cabbage,
He refused to eat the beans.
Sometimes he was very rude,
Said cauliflowers were yuk.
He called the carrots Donkey Food
And would not eat them up.

This state of things went on until
Cornelius would go
And turn on the television
To see a cartoon show.

Popeye the sailor-man was on,
He was very strong and tough
'Cause he ate whole tins of spinach
And thought it was jolly good stuff.
From then on Cornelius pondered –
Perhaps he had been very wrong –
So he ate all the green stuff they gave him
And grew up to be big and strong.

'Oh dear,' said the small Bunny Rabbit,
'We always have lettuce for tea,
A dandelion head would be nicer instead,
What a wonderful change it would be.'
'Oh, let us eat lettuce,' said Mother,
'For lettuce is good for a rabbit.
A lettuce a day in the usual way
Becomes you will find, a good habit.'

There was a mouse, a sorry mouse,
He had a mouse-hole in our house.
He had a wife and children four
And a cousin mouse who lived next-door.
One sunny day he wandered out
To see what food lay round about.
He saw some cheese, 'twas in a trap.
He poked his nose in. Silly chap.
Then in a flash, the story goes,
The trap sprang down upon his nose,
It gave him such a heavy clout
It hurt and knocked his teeth right out.
Though he wriggled free, it's understood
It didn't do our mouse much good.
Though our hero isn't dead,
Not a single tooth stayed in his head.
So, should you meet him do not tease,
Don't offer him hard mousetrap cheese
But just the sort that spreads with ease.

Little Jack Horner sat in the corner
Eating a plum-duff pie.
He took out a plum,
Bit a hole in his thumb,
And that's when he started to cry.

I painted a beautiful picture
With some paints that I found on a shelf.
But when I had finished I noticed
I had painted a lot of myself.
My fingers were green and the tip of my nose
Was a mixture of yellow and pink.
My clothes were a mess, but no doubt you can
    guess,
That I washed it all off in the sink.

Today I tidied up my toys,
I had to, there's no doubt.
The cupboard door refused to shut
And the toys kept falling out.
So I put them away quite neatly,
I could only just close the door,
But what shall I do on my birthday
If I get a whole lot more?

146

The ship sailed across the ocean
On its journey to Samarkand.
Would it reach the harbour safely
In that far and distant land?
Then the storm clouds began to gather
And the waves grew high and wide.
The ship was in trouble and failing,
Then it sank neath that mighty tide.
It lay on the floor of the ocean,
A prey of the sea's mighty wrath,
Then along came a diver and rescued the ship
From the bottom of my bath.

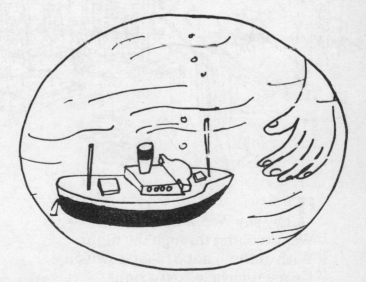

They say Wee Willie Winkie
Went rushing through the night
With nothing but a night-gown on –
He must have looked a sight.

There was a baby kangaroo
With very little else to do
But clamber up into his mother's pouch.

Mrs Kangaroo cried 'Ouch'
Because, of course, it must be told,
Although she loved her baby
His feet were very cold.

The warthog is a vulgar sort of animal,
It grunts and snorts and snuffles in the ground.
It's not the sort of animal to cuddle
And the nicest people don't want one around.

A teddy bear is soft and warm,
You can cuddle him in bed.
A puppy dog is cute and likes
To be stroked upon his head.
A kitten has fur as soft as silk
And a gerbil is just as fine.
I love my pet, but I don't know yet
How to cuddle my porcupine.

The walrus is not pretty,
He would make an awkward pet.
If you took him to bed to cuddle
Your pyjamas would get wet.

I hear a buzzing in the gloom,
A fly is flitting round my room.
It buzzes loudly round my head,
Just one quick swipe, I have it . . . dead.

I wonder sometimes what it is
That makes me love it so.
It hasn't really got a shape,
It's sort of 'so and so'.
It's brown with yellow patches,
It's not a teddy bear,
It isn't really anything
That you'd find anywhere.
It's not a kind of elephant,
It hasn't got a trunk,
It isn't stripy black and white,
It cannot be a skunk.
It has a leg and just one eye
In a battered sort of face,
I think it's just the sort of thing
To come from outer space.
It sleeps in bed beside me –
Never, never on the shelf.
I love it so, because you know
I made it all myself.

Shining star, shining bright,
I wish you could,
I wish you might,
Make my wish come true tonight.